C000282951

kisses and caresses

Alex Comfort M.B., D.Sc.

Illustrated by
John Raynes

Mitchell Beazley

The JOY OF SEX ® Series

First published in 1997 by Mitchell Beazley,
an imprint of Reed International Books Limited,
Michelin House, 81 Fulham Road, London SW3 6RB
and Auckland, Melbourne, Singapore and Toronto

Copyright © 1997 Mitchell Beazley

All rights reserved. No part of this work may be reproduced
or utilized in any form or by any means, electronic or mechanical,
including photocopying, recording or by any information storage
and retrieval system, without prior written permission of the publisher.

ISBN 1 85732 6784

A CIP catalogue record for this book
is available from the British Library

Produced by Mandarin Offset
Printed and bound in Hong Kong

c o n t e n t s

introduction

ar too many people are tempted to think of kisses and caresses as a kind of sub-sexual activity, suitable for early dates, but something they can give up on when they graduate to a 'proper' sexual relationship. Some of the kisses and caresses described here are indeed things one uses in the early stages of a relationship, or as a preliminary to greater adventure, but all of them are part of the repertoire of lovers, and always will be. *Kisses and Caresses* sets out to show that kisses, along with caresses of varying degrees of intimacy and adventurousness, have an important part to play in even the most exuberant and sophisticated sex life.

This 'pillow book' singles these expressions of affection out for attention, encouraging lovers not to treat them as an isolated, even clinical sideshow, but rather as a key part of the seamless whole of sex and its enjoyment. This area of lovemaking is also placed firmly in the context of the total enjoyment of a sexual relationship, while the selection also emphasizes the roles of love, tenderness and fidelity in any truly fulfilling partnership.

Compared with our ancestors, too many of us tend to rush into sex without exploring the currency of love, or using its accessories to the full. What's more, many writers about sex now concentrate on the most obvious and dramatic achievements instead of reminding those eager to learn and experiment that blunt instruments are not always the most effective. For this reason, we commend these kisses and caresses to patient, caring but adventurous people who want to improve their skills as lovemakers; those true lovers who already know many of the techniques will not resent sharing them.

Begin with the simpler, more straightforward kisses and caresses shown in this book before, at your own speed, graduating on to more varied varieties of sensual experience in this area of lovemaking.

Alex Comfort

Alex Comfort M.B., D.Sc.

love

We use the same word for man–woman, mother–child, child–parent, and I–mankind relations – rightly, because they are a continuous spectrum. In talking about sexual relations, it seems right to apply it to any relationship in which there is mutual tenderness, respect and consideration – from a total interdependence where the death of one maims the other for

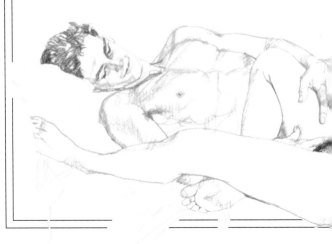

years, to an agreeable night together. The intergrades are all love, all worthy, all part of human experience.

Some meet the needs of one person, some of another – or of the same person at different times. That's really the big problem of sexual ethics, and it's basically a problem of self-understanding and of communication. You can't assume that your 'conditions of love' are applicable to, or accepted by, any other party; you can't assume that these won't be changed quite unpredictably in both of you by the experience of loving; you can't necessarily know your own mind.

love . . . *the essential openness of a real relationship between people . . .*

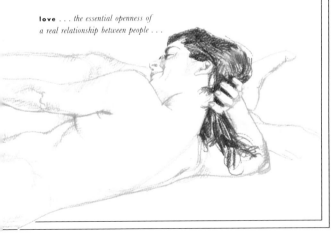

f sexual love can be – and it is – the supreme human experience, it must be also a bit hazardous. It can give us our best and our worst moments. In this respect it's like mountain climbing – over-timid people miss the whole experience; reasonably balanced and hardy people accept the risks for the rewards, but realize that there's a difference between this and being foolhardy. Love, moreover, involves someone else's neck beside your own. At least you can make as sure as may be that you don't exploit or injure someone. Getting them to sign a form of consent before they start isn't the answer either. There was a hell of a lot to be said for the English Victorian idea of not being a cad ('person devoid of finer or gentlemanly feelings'). A cad can be of either sex.

Marriage between two rival actor-managers, each trying to produce the other regardless, isn't love. The relationship between a prostitute and a casual client where, for reasons they don't quite get, real tenderness and respect occur, is.

love *A potentially overwhelming experience worth all the risks*

t e n d e r n e s s

*T*enderness doesn't exclude extremely violent games (though many people neither need nor want these), but it does exclude clumsiness, heavy handedness, lack of feedback, spitefulness and non-rapport generally, shown fully in the way you touch each other. What it implies at root is a constant awareness of what your partner is feeling, plus the knowledge of how to heighten that feeling, gently, toughly, slowly or fast, and this only comes from an inner state of mind between you. No really tender person can just turn over and go to sleep.

Many if not most inexperienced men, and some women, are just naturally clumsy – either through haste, through anxiety, or through lack of sensing how the other sex feels. Men in general are harder-skinned than women – don't grab breasts, stick fingers

tenderness *What it implies is a constant awareness of what your partner is feeling*

tenderness *Gently does it can be exciting for both of you*

into the vagina, handle female skin as if it was your own, or (and this goes for both sexes) misplace bony parts of your anatomy. More girls respond to very light than to very heavy stimulation – just brushing pubic hair or skin hairs will usually do far more than a whole-hand grab. At the same time don't be frightened – neither of you is made of glass. Women by contrast often fail to use enough pressure, especially in handwork, though the light, light variety is a sensation on its own. Start very gently, making full use of the skin surface, and work up. Stimulus toleration in any case increases with sexual excitement until even hard blows can become excitants (though not for everyone). This loss of pain sense disappears almost instantly with orgasm, so don't go on too long, and be extra gentle as soon as he or she has come.

If you are really heavy-handed, a little practice with inanimate surfaces, dress-fastenings and so on will help. Male strength is a turn-on in sex, but it isn't expressed in clumsy handwork, bear-hugs and brute force – at least not as starters. If there is a problem here, remember you both can talk. Few people want to be in bed on any terms with a person who isn't basically tender, and most people are delighted to be in bed with the right person who is. The ultimate test is whether you can bear to find the person there when you wake up. If you are actually pleased, then you're onto the right thing.

f i d e l i t y

idelity, infidelity, jealousy and so on. We've deliberately not gone into the ethics of lifestyle. The facts are that few men and slightly more women in our culture go through life with sexual experience confined to one partner only. What suits a particular couple depends on their needs, situation, anxieties and so on. These needs are a particularly delicate problem in communication: if mutual comprehension is complete and ongoing you can count yourselves lucky. Active deception always hurts a relationship. Complete frankness which is aimed to avoid guilt or as an act of aggression against a partner can do the same. The real problem arises from the fact that sexual relations can be anything, for different people on different occasions, from a game to a total fusion of identities; the heartaches arise when

fidelity *In a relationship this means that you know where each of you stands*

each partner sees it differently. There is no sexual relationship which doesn't involve responsibility, because there are two or more people involved: anything which, as it were, militantly excludes a partner is hurtful, yet to be whole people we have at some point to avoid total fusion with each other – 'I am I and you are you, and neither of us is on earth to live up to the other's expectations.' People who communicate sexually have to find their own fidelities. All we can suggest is that you discuss them so that at least you know where each of you stands.

fidelity *All relationships involve responsibility to yourself and to each other*

k i s s e s

hese, at one level, don't require teaching, but it's easy to be so set on insertion that one overlooks them. Lip and tongue kisses add immensely to intercourse in all face-to-face positions; breast kisses are essential if the woman isn't to miss a whole range of feeling; genital kisses are a tender resource on their own. Kisses can be put anywhere on the body, they can be given with lips, tongue, penis, labia or eyelashes – mouth kisses range from a mere touch to the kiss *à la cannibale*, which leaves a bruise.

A lot of people maintain mouth contact continuously throughout intercourse, and prefer face-to-face positions for this reason. The deep tongue kiss can either be a second penetration, the man's tongue imitating exactly the rhythm of what is going on elsewhere, or she can give it, penetrating him, to call the rhythm.

kisses *These should leave you breathless*

19

ven without any penetration, some people favour a
tongue-battle which can last minutes or even hours, bringing
several orgasms for the girl: this form of non-genital heavy petting
is called *maraîchignage*.

Another pleasure is to make her a carpet of flowers, by covering every inch of her body with small, close kisses. From there
it is only a little way to doing the same with a tongue-tip (see
tongue bath): moreover, unlike a man, she has two mouths to
kiss with, and some women use them beautifully. Eyelids too can
be used for nipple, lip, glans and skin kisses.

If you haven't at least kissed her mouth, shoulders, neck,
breasts, armpits, fingers, palms, toes, soles, navel, genitals and
earlobes, you haven't really kissed her: it is no trouble to fill in the
gaps for completeness and makes a touching compliment.

A good mouth kiss should leave its recipient breathless but
not asphyxiated (leave an airway open), and nobody likes their
nose squashed into their face. Clean your teeth before making
love, and if you are having whisky, garlic, pickled onions, etc,
both of you have it.

kisses *Move on to make her a carpet of flowers by covering her body with close kisses*

b r e a s t s

n our maturer years,' wrote Darwin, 'when an object of vision is presented to us which bears any similitude to the form of the female bosom . . . we feel a general glow of delight which seems to influence all our senses, and if the object be not too large we experience an attraction to embrace it with our lips as we did in early infancy the bosom of our mothers.' Alfred Perles greeted a socialite who was seated next to him at a dinner table with the words 'those aren't bad – fish them out and let's have a look at them.' Breasts are the natural second target, but often the first one that we reach. Just how sensitive they are, in men as well as in women, varies enormously from person to person – size is unimportant, as with other sexual organs. Some don't answer at all, even in the emphatically non-frigid; some answer to extremely gentle touches, some to very rough handling (but they are sensitive structures – don't let your residual anger at having been weaned get the better of your commonsense).

breasts *One can get a surprising degree of mutuality from intermammary intercourse*

23

R*ound and round the nipple* with the tongue tip or the glans, soft kneading with both hands, gentle biting and sucking gently like a baby are the best gambits. She can use these on the man, plus very gentle fingertip friction – men's nipples easily get sore, however. If her breasts are big enough to meet, one can get a surprising degree of mutuality from intermammary intercourse. Lay her half flat on pillows, kneel astride (big toe to her clitoris if she needs helping) and your foreskin fully retracted. Either you or she can hold the breasts

breasts *She says 'Men are in too much of a hurry to get lower down. Please take time'*

25

together – wrap them around the shaft rather than rub the glans with them. It should protrude clear, just below her chin.

Breasts, vagina and clitoris all at once make the most concentrated and fastest buildup of sensation once intercourse has begun, for some women at least. Few men can get a nipple orgasm, but a stiff pair of feathers is worth trying. Many easily stimulated or well loved women can get a rather special pleasure from suckling a baby.

She says: 'Men still don't understand about breasts, or are in too much of a hurry to get lower down – unlike a man's nipples, a woman's have a direct hot line to her clitoris. A man who can dial this correctly and will only take the time can do anything. Palm-brushing, eyelid-brushing, licking, and loud sucking like a baby can work wonders; the orgasms one gets from these are mind-blowing, without detracting a jot from intercourse to come after. Please take time.'

breasts *Her nipples have a direct link to her clitoris, so spend time on them*

buttocks

ext in line after breasts, buttocks alternate with them as visual sex stimuli for different cultures and individuals. Actually the original primate focus, being brightly colored in most apes: apparently equally fancied by the Mousterian culture which produced some of the best Stone Age figurines, while more recent primitives 'made their selection by ranging from women in a line and picking her out who projects furthest *a tergo*' (Darwin). Visually, good buttocks are a turn-on.

The buttocks are a major erogenous zone in both sexes, less sensitive than breasts because they contain muscle as well as fat, and needing stronger stimulation (holding, kneading, slapping or even harder beating).

buttocks *A major erogenous zone*
and turn-on for both sexes

tongue bath

oing systematically over every square inch of a
partner, tied if they like, with long, slow, broad tongue
strokes. Start behind, turn them and cover the front surface
after, so as to be in position to go on to coition or

hand- and mouthwork. If the woman gives this, she follows it by covering the whole available surface equally systematically with slow strokes of her open vulva. Mini-versions cover particular areas in the same way.

tongue bath *Slow, all-over arousal*

b l o w i n g

ot in the slang sense but quite simply making a current of air on the (preferably pre-wetted, see *tongue bath* on pages 30-31) skin of any part of the body, either from the lips or from a hairdrier with the heat turned off. The best way to moisten an erogenous area is with long, broad strokes of the tongue, though for more extensive operations one can obviously use water or lotion instead. A gentle stream of air on a wet sensitive surface produces a sensation which can drive some people of either sex out of their minds – experiment on sensitive areas on a small scale, using your natural equipment (saliva and breath).

In the case of earlobes, breathe in, not out, or you'll deafen your partner. Elsewhere use steady continuous exhalation with the

blowing *A mind-blowing sensation on skin that has been tongue-bathed*

lips about an inch from the skin. For a bigger operation, use the hairdrier – the result is far wilder than the conventional routine with feathers (see pages 40-41) – try mixing the two by hitching a couple of feathers to the drier nozzle on threads. Never use a strong air source, and never blow into the vagina or any other body orifice (except the mouth): the former is particularly important as you could cause an embolism and accidentally kill her.

blowing *The best way to moisten an erogenous area is with the tongue*

35

p a t t e s d'a r a i g n é e

*P*attes d'araignée, literally 'spider's legs', is tickling erotic massage, using the pulps of the fingers, with the *lightest possible touch*, aiming to stimulate not so much the skin as the almost invisible skin-hairs: not on the genitals, but all the next most

pattes d'araignée *Erotic massage at its most delicate*

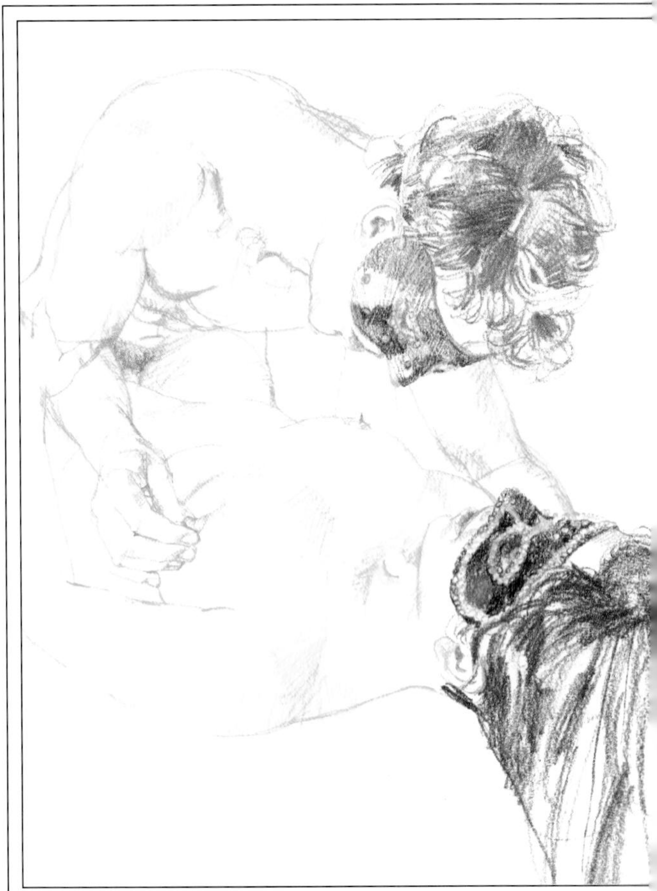

sensitive places – nipples and around, neck, chest, belly, insides of arms and thighs, armpits, hollow of the back, soles and palms, scrotum, space between it and the anus. Use both hands; keep a steady progression of movement going with one, and make surprise attacks with the other.

The whole essence is in the extreme lightness of the touch – which is more electric than tickling. Using feathers, bristlegloves or vibrators gives a quite different sensation. If you are agile, don't forget you have toes as well as fingers and hair in various places on your body, including your eyelids, to vary the sensation. A set of finger-cots with textures ranging from cardcloth to mink are easy to use; the real and original French style with the fingertips is difficult to learn but unforgettable by either sex. It's one of the two general skin stimulants (the other is the *tongue bath*) which work even on not very skin-conscious males.

pattes d'araignée *Her skin is super-sensitive
and will respond to the lightest of touches*

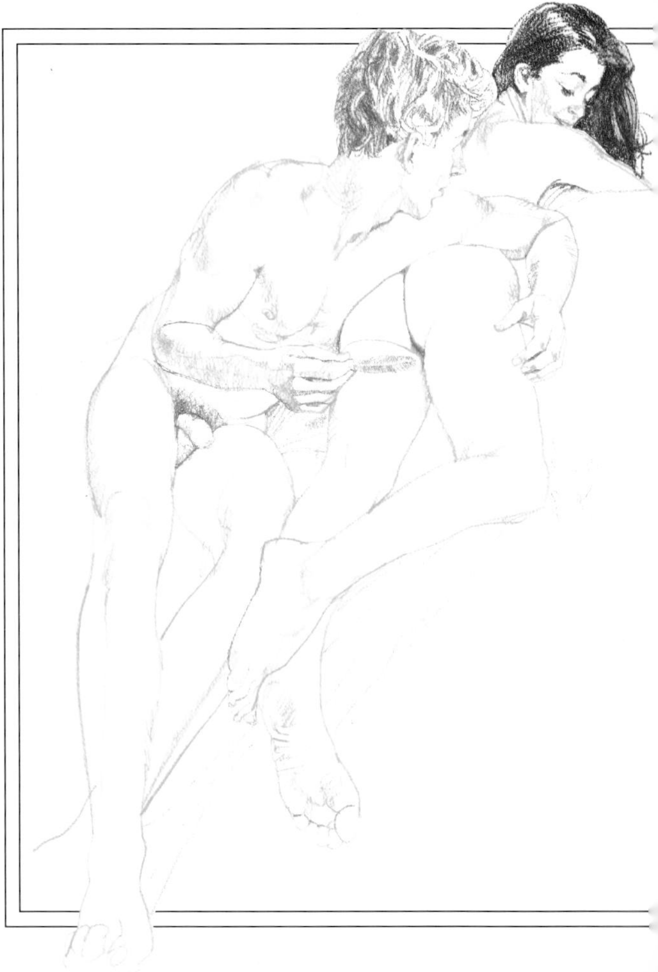

feathers

Recommended by some for skin stimulation (breasts, body surface generally, more than actual genitals and palms and soles). Try stiff wiry ones (heron or egret) or those from an old fashioned feather duster.

feathers *Alternate them with mouth music and tongue bathing*

skin

kin is our chief extragenital sexual organ. Not only its feel when touched, but its coolness, texture and tightness are triggers for a whole range of sexual feelings. These can be boosted in some people by emphasis, and by adding other textures, especially fur, rubber, leather or tight clothing. Much under-rated part of human sexual response, to be played to the full if it turns you on.

skin *Its importance as a sex organ is grossly underrated by men; women not only understand it better but rate it much higher*

43

h a i r

ead hair has a lot of Freudian overtones – in ancient mythology it's a sign of virility, witness Samson or Hercules, and some of these associations persist.

Our culture having learned in previous generations to associate long hair with women and short hair with manly conformity has been occasionally excited to frenzy when young males rejected the stereotype and wore their hair, in the words of the seventeenth–century Harvard MS 'in the manner of ruffians and barbarous Indians' – or of George Washington. Freud thought that long female hair acted as reassurance to the male by being a substitute for the phallus women don't have. Be that as it may, long male hair in our generation tends to go with a less anxious idea of maleness.

hair *Long hair in her can be a turn-on for him and she can use it as a skin-stimulant*

S ex play with long hair is great because of its texture — you can handle it, touch each other with it, and generally use it as one more resource. Some women are turned on by a fair amount of masculine body hair because it looks virile, others turned off by it because it looks animal — this seems to be a matter of attitude.

M *ale face hair* is another focus of convention – sometimes everyone has it as a social necessity or a
response to convention, at other times it is persecuted, or confined
to sailors, pioneers and exotic people such as artists and chefs.
Schopenhauer thought that it covered the parts of the face 'which
express the moral feelings', and disapproved on the grounds that
it was immodest to wear a sex signal in the middle of one's face.
Today you can please yourself, or better, your partner.

p u b i c   h a i r

*S*have *it off if you prefer*. If you do shave it, you're committed to a prickly interregnum while it regrows.

It can be combed, twirled, kissed, even pulled. In the woman it can move the whole pubis, skillfully handled, to the point of orgasm. For the woman, it's often best not to shave but to

pubic hair *Most lovers regard it as an additional resource, not an embarrassment to be shaved off*

pubic hair
*Try trimming it so
that it is entirely
covered by a g-string*

50

trim, confining the triangle to the middle of
the pubis with a bare strip each side – the
pattern of youth – removing hair which
comes outside a g-string or bathing
slip, and trimming enough to make
the vulva fully visible.

Men can shave if they like,
or their partners like, but
it's difficult to shave the
scrotum. You may need
to shave the penile shaft
and root to use condoms
– otherwise the hairs
can get rolled in.

pubic hair
*Try brushing it lightly
with your mouth or
kissing it – it holds
her scent and will
drive her wild*

e a r l o b e s

*U*nderrated erogenous zone, together with the adjacent neck skin – the small area behind the ear has a hot line to the visceral nerves via the vagus – and the nape of the neck. As with all extragenital sites, they are more effective in women than men. Once established (gentle fingering, sucking, etc, during buildup and before orgasm, to condition the response) earlobes can trigger full climax from manipulation alone. Some women find the noise of heavy breathing excruciating and a definite turn-off, so be careful.

Heavy earrings help, and can actually maintain subliminal erotic excitement, especially if long enough to brush the neck when she turn her head – this is the function of the large oriental and Spanish candelabra-type earrings.

earlobes *Dramatic results are obtainable, but not with heavy breathing!*

he sex difference in response probably accounts for their relative rarity worldwide in male fashions. Swinging weights as erotic stimuli to a particular area aren't confined to the ears. If earrings are the screw-on type, take them off and try them gently on her nipples, labia or clitoris.

n a v e l

ascinating to all lovers, like all the details of the human body.
It's not only decorative but sensitive and has a lot of cultivable visual and tactile sexual sensation; it fits the finger, tongue, glans or big toe, and merits careful attention when you kiss or touch or as part of a *tongue bath*. Intercourse in the navel is practicable (there are stories of some naive couples who thought that this was the usual way, and it's a common childhood fantasy about how sex is conducted, as well as where babies come from). If she is plump she can hold up the skin on each side of the navel to make a surrogate labia. It may also be a possiblility as a menstrual alternative. In any case, the finger or tongue tip slip into it naturally in both sexes.

navel *To kiss or touch, with, even,
possibilities of intercourse*

a r m p i t

lassic site for kisses. Should on
no account be shaved. Can be used
instead of the palm to silence your partner
at climax – if you use your palm, rub
it over your own or your partner's
armpit area first.

armpit *A classic site for perfumed kisses*

57

Axillary intercourse is an occasional variation. Handle it as for intermammary intercourse (see *breasts*) but with your penis under her right arm – well under, so that friction is on the shaft, not the glans, as in any other unlubricated area. Put her left arm round your neck and hold her right hand behind her with your right hand. She will get sensations from the pressure against her breasts, helped by your big toe pressed to her clitoris if she wants it. Not an outstandingly rewarding trick but worth trying if you like the idea.

armpit *If unshaven it will retain her scent better*

feet

Very attractive sexually to some people – he can get an orgasm, if wished, between her soles. Their erotic sensitivity varies a lot. Sometimes, when they're the only part you can reach, they serve as channels of communication, and the big toe is a good penis substitute.

feet *The feet can be kissed, sucked, tickled,*
or tied with stimulating results

*T*ickling the soles excites some people out of their minds; for others it's agony but increases general arousal. You can try it as a stimulus, or, briefly, for testing bondage. Firm pressure on the sole at the instep, however administered, is erogenic to most people. But so can almost any touch be in a woman who's that way minded – one can get a full orgasm from a foot, a finger, or an earlobe. Men respond less far but equally easily if the handling is skillful.

62

big toe

The pad of the male big toe applied to the clitoris or the vulva generally is a magnificent erotic instrument. The famous gentleman in erotic prints who is keeping six women occupied is using tongue, penis, both hands and both big toes.

big toe *A sexual organ of considerable versatility, yielding great pleasure*